LORD BUDDHA STORIES FOR KIDS- INSPIRING STORIES FROM THE LIFE OF BUDDHA

THIS BOOK BELONGS TO

_____

_____

_____

A long time ago there was a kingdom in North India called Kapilavastu. It was this kingdom that gave us the buddha, the illumined one, who played a key part in changing the world's perception of life and its problems. King Shudhodhana who belonged to Sakya clan ruled the kingdom. Mahamaya was his Queen.

King and Queen were sleeping inside the palace and Queen Mahamaya see a dream while she was in deep sleep and she starts murmuring in sleep.

KING SHUDHODHANA – Mahamaya, O Mahamaya…

QUEEN MAHAMAYA- Oh dear, where am I?

KING SHUDHODHANA – What happened dear? you were saying something?

QUEEN MAHAMAYA- Ah yes, I had a dream. a divine dream.

KING SHUDHODHANA – Dreams at this early hour come true.

QUEEN MAHAMAYA- Hmm. the sky was filled with white light and a bunch of rays became a white elephant with six tusks and it entered my room. I feel happy and my heart is filled with joy.

KING SHUDHODHANA– Amazing I will ask our Royal astrologer to interpret this dream.

ASTROLOGER- King I have interpreted our queens dream. this kingdom is going to have a great Prince. the Queen will bear a son who will become a great man. one day the whole world will be benefited by the prince.

KING SHUDHODHANA – Thank God, my dream has come true. I am going to have a son who will succeed me. Months rolled by.

QUEEN MAHAMAYA- Dear as is the custom I would like to go to my parent's house to give birth.

KING SHUDHODHANA – As you wish. I will arrange for your journey. take care dear.

The Queen and her attendants began their journey to the home of her childhood.

QUEEN MAHAMAYA- Oh… I am so tired. where are we? oh what a beautiful place, let's get down and rest here for some time. I think the baby is ready to come into this world.

Unlike other women Mahamaya delivered her child while standing and holding on to the tree branch. Mahamaya gave birth to a noble prince, destined to be the greatest spiritual teacher of the world in the Lumbini Park on the full moon day of May.

Siddhartha immediately took seven steps. at each step a lotus grew out of the ground to receive the future Budha. The infant arose, pointing one finger to the heavens and one to the earth, declaring, in the heavens and on the earth.

SIDHARTHA- I am the most venerable teacher of gods and man. This is my last birth on this earth.

The attendants were astonished and were filled with Wonder by the child's beauty.

QUEEN MAHAMAYA- Oh what a serene face? let's go back to Kapilavastu. The king will be longing to see his son.

Mahamaya returned with her son to Kapilavastu. That news about the birth of the Prince spread everywhere.

KING SHUDHODHANA – Arrange for a grand reception. My son is coming.

QUEEN MAHAMAYA- Dear look at our son.

KING SHUDHODHANA – Beautiful, welcome home my son. let's go in. do we need to give him a name?

QUEEN MAHAMAYA- Yeah. I'm thinking of name Siddharth. how is the name Siddharth?

KING SHUDHODHANA – Siddharth, a lovely name. It means wish fulfilled. okay now let him sleep.

Next day the ceremony took place in a grand way. meantime a great sage Asita who had given up the worldly pleasures heard about the birth of Sidhartha.

SAGE ASITA- Let me visit kings palace.

KING SHUDHODHANA – Look there. welcome to great sage. we are really blessed.

QUEEN MAHAMAYA- Welcome o great sage. please bless our child.

SAGE ASITA- Let me bless your son.

Great sage Asita instead of blessing the child saluted it. First, he felt happy and then sand.

KING SHUDHODHANA – Sage what is this?

SAGE ASITA- O king, your son is not an ordinary child. I am sure he will grow up to be more than a great man. if the Prince stayed with you and wanted to rule the kingdom, he would become the greatest king ever. he would rule a huge Kingdom and his people would have peace and much joy. but if he made the decision not to become a king, his future would be will greater. he will become a great teacher who would show the people the way to live with their hearts filled with love and peace.

KING SHUDHODHANA – Thank you. but why were you first happy and then sad.

SAGE ASITA- I was happy because he would become a great teacher and sad, I would not be alive to benefit from his superior wisdom. I will take leave now.

QUEEN MAHAMAYA- I want my son to be a great ruler and not a teacher.

The beloved Queen died seven days after giving birth to her child. her younger sister, Mahaprajapati who was also married to the king adopted the child and took good care of him.

Years rolled by. The prince grew into a bright, handsome and kind-hearted boy.

KING SHUDHODHANA – It's time for me to arrange for his education. I will appoint the best teachers in the kingdom for him.

Few days passed.

MASTER- (He is remarkably intelligent. there is nothing I can teach him. let me convey this to our King)

KING SHUDHODHANA – Oh welcome teacher. how is my son doing in studies?

MASTER- Your majesty, the prince does not need us anymore. after only a few lessons he has learned everything. we have to teach him; in fact, he has taught us a few things that we ourselves never knew before. I am really proud of him with his intelligence.

KING SHUDHODHANA – My son will certainly grow up to be a wise and powerful King. son why don't you go and play with the other boys.

SIDHARTHA- Father, they are quarreling with each other. I do not like it. I love to spend my time in peace.

Siddhartha always played with the animals and spent much of his time alone. one day as the prince was sitting in the garden, a flock of white swans flew overhead. Suddenly an arrow shot up into the air, striking one of them. The stricken bird fell out of the sky and landed in the garden. Sidhartha gently picked up the swan.

SIDHARTHA- Oh you poor a swan, do not be afraid. I shall take care of you. here let me remove this arrow and pull this medicine juice. now you will be out of danger.

Devadatta cousin of Siddharth came running into the garden and said

DEVADATTA- Sidharth, great news! got a swan! you should have seen my aim. I hit it with my first shot. it fell down somewhere near here. help me, look for it. what this is my arrow? where is my bird?

SIDHARTHA- It's with me.

DEVADATTA- Yeah, I can see it. you took my Swan. give it back to me. I shot it and its mine.

SIDHARTHA- Don't ever touch it. I found this bird lying here bleeding and I don't plan to give it to anyone, while it is still wounded.

DEVADATTA- It belongs to me. I shot it fair and square and you have stolen it from me. give it back or I will take it back.

SIDHARTHA- It belongs to the sky and should be set free to go on its way as soon as it is able to fly. until it recovers, it is mine. since I saved its life.

The two brothers stood arguing like this for some time. Devadatta was getting angrier and angrier. but Siddhartha refused to give him the swan. when two grown-ups quarrel like this, they settle it in court. In front of a group of wise people each one explains his case. then the wise people decide who is right.

SIDHARTHA- I think you and I should do the same.

DEVADATTA- I don't like this idea very much. but I agree because this is the only way I can get my Swan back.

So, the two of them went to the palace and appeared in front of the king and his ministers.

SIDHARTHA- Father we are here to settle our dispute over the swan.

KING SHUDHODHANA – Let me hear your story first. First is Devadatta's chance.

Both gave their sides of the story. the court was also divided and could not arrive at a unanimous verdict. then a very old man came to the court, but no one remember him or ever seen before. he looks very wise. he will be in a position to give a verdict.

OLDMAN- Everyone values his or her life more than anything else in the world. Therefore, I think that the swan belongs to the person who tried to save its life, not the person who tried to take its life away. So, the swan rightfully belongs to Siddharth.

Everyone agreed that what the wise man said was true. so, they decided to let the Prince keep the swan. later when the king tried to find the old man and reward him for his wisdom he was nowhere to be found.

KING SHUDHODHANA – This is very strange. I wonder where he came from and where he went.

This was just one of the many unusual things that happened concerning the prince. so many people thought he must be a very special person indeed.

On coming of age, the Prince became famous and was loved by everyone because of his kind and peaceful nature. but King was much worried about him.

King Shudhodhana discuss with his minister about nature of Sidhartha.

KING SHUDHODHANA – A king without Drive and daring how could that be? Minister Siddharth is too gentle and sensitive. I want him to grow up to be a great King. Kings must be strong and powerful. he is more interested in sitting peacefully in the garden, than he is in learning. how to be the ruler of a kingdom?

MINISTER- Do not worry. we will look for a way to change our prince.

KING SHUDHODHANA – If he becomes a great teacher, as sage Asita predicted, my wish of his becoming a great king will remain unfulfilled.

MINISTER- King I have a suggestion, the prince should be married, to get him out of his dream world and into the real world.

KING SHUDHODHANA – Hope this idea will work out. let's start our search for a beautiful princess worthy of my son.

Days passed.

MINISTER- My lord, I suggest that princess Yashodhara, daughter of King Suprabuddha will be a perfect match.

KING SHUDHODHANA – Then let me start immediately.

King Shudhodhana visits palace of Suprabudha.

KING SUPRABUDHA- Welcome, we are honored by your visit. tell me your great one.

KING SHUDHODHANA – Thanks for your great welcome. we are here to talk about an important proposal. we are here to ask your daughter's hand for our Prince Siddhartha.

KING SUPRABUDHA- I would like to tell you that there are lots of other excellent young men who want to marry my daughter. I will arrange for a contest. the prince should compete to marry my daughter.

KING SHUDHODHANA – I agree.

KING SHUDHODHANA – Minister my worries have doubled now. Siddharth had never shown the slightest liking for warrior games. then how will he win among skilled contestants?

SIDHARTHA- Do not worry father. I will win the contest. I will do whatever is required to make Yashodhara my pride.

The day of the contest arrived and Sidhartha participated along with other Prince's.

SOLDIERS- The first contest will be archery.

Sidhartha was excelled in it.

SOLDIERS- The second contest the swordsmanship. the third is Horse riding.

Though there were many skilled contestants Sidhartha excelled in the sports and won his lady's hand, not only by show of strength but also with his tender and caring nature.

KING SHUDHODHANA – Let's announce the marriage of Prince Siddharth with Princess Yashodhara.

MINISTER- To make our Prince engage in normal life, we need to keep him happy.

KING SHUDHODHANA – Yes. let's make the necessary arrangements.

The marriage was held with great pomp and show.

KING SHUDHODHANA – On this occasion, I gift you three wonderful palaces. Rama palace for winter season. Sarama palace for summer season and Subha palace for rainy season. see to it that he's entertained the whole day and not allowed to see anything sad, unpleasant or pathetic.

For many years Siddharth lived a luxurious life.

KING SHUDHODHANA – My plans are working out so well.

After dinner the prince would relax by listening to sweet relaxing melodies.

SIDHARTHA- Oh I feel Restless today. O great singer will you sing a song, you have never sung before.

The singer sang of the beauties of the world, of her travels to faraway places of happy people who lived in golden cities.

KING SHUDHODHANA – I would like to know whether there are such beautiful places as described in the song. beyond the garden walls. I think I have lots of things to explore this mysterious world. let me talk to my father.

KING SHUDHODHANA – Son come dear.

SIDHARTHA- Yes, Father, I am curious to see the outside world. I feel as if I have been caged in the palace, totally unaware of all the wonders of the world. I want to go out and see the outside world. please arrange for a trip outside the palace.

KING SHUDHODHANA – That, son…. my suggestion is…

SIDHARTHA- Please do not give any excuses. arrange for a trip.

KING SHUDHODHANA – Okay son.

King Shudhodhana meets his minister to discuss about Sidhartha.

KING SHUDHODHANA – Minister. did you hear this. Siddhartha has requested for a trip and I have accepted it. if I say no, then his eagerness will grow.

MINISTER- He should not encounter any unpleasant thing.

KING SHUDHODHANA – Yes, you are right. let's do it this way, we will pass an order that everyone should decorate their houses and look happy.

Next day Channa the charioteer bushed up Kantaka, the prince's favorite horse and drove to the capital city.

SIDHARTHA- Ah! first glimpse of Kapilavastu.

The whole kingdom came on the streets to take their first look of the handsome young prince.

PEOPLE- We are really fortunate, one day he will rule us.

PEOPLE- Yes, long live our Prince.

SIDHARTHA- Channa, everyone is happy. I see a smile on everyone's face. The song was right. This is a beautiful and wonderful city. Channa why is that man so different from the others?

CHANNA- Where dear prince?

SIDHARTHA- Over there in the crowd.

CHANNA- Oh he's an old man.

SIDHARTHA- Old meaning.

CHANNA- Meaning, his days are over. he too was young and healthy like others used before. but slowly his strength was lost and as a result his body got bent, his cheeks lost their color. he lost most of his teeth.

SIDHARTHA- Well. Like him I too become old? my father too become old.

CHANNA- Yes Prince. everyone will become old.

SIDHARTHA- Yashodhara?

CHANNA- Princes, Prince Rahul, everyone. everyone born on this earth will become old. every moment of everyday a person grows older.

SIDHARTHA- I am shocked. this is the cruel reality of life. I'm scared. my trip has been spoiled. let's go back. go back Channa.

CHANNA- We will.

Yashodhara tried to lift his spirits. but was unsuccessful. he did not eat anything and sat alone pondering over old age. the next day,

KING SHUDHODHANA – Minister let's arrange for another trip. this time strict care has to be taken to keep our prince happy.

MINISTER- As you say my lord.

Channa and Sidhartha went on chariot.

SIDHARTHA- Channa, the people seem so happy. Happy… stop…. stop the chariot.

CHANNA- Yes, Prince.

SIDHARTHA- Come with me. can you see there. why is the man lying on the road?

CHANNA- Prince, he is a sick man.

SIDHARTHA- Why is he giving out such strange sounds?

CHANNA- Prince. he is coughing. he is ill.

SIDHARTHA- What has brought him to this pass?

CHANNA- There are a number of reasons. but his body has grown weak and he is no more able to resist their illnesses that visit one.

SIDHARTHA- Will all the happy people become sick one day.

CHANNA- Yes Prince and no one has saved from illness.

SIDHARTHA- I am totally depressed. I don't understand how people can be so happy when they could become sick any moment. let's go back Channa.

The prince was even more depressed and did not speak to anyone.

MINISTER- Lord, our prince is not as usual self. he has been greatly disturbed.

KING SHUDHODHANA – I pray to God that my fear should not come true. this time he should not see any site that will disturb him the least.

Again, the city wore of festival and people were happy.

CHANNA- Prince forget what you saw yesterday. see there, how beautiful those children are. turned aside for a lovely garden.

SIDHARTHA- Yes. but stop Channa.

CHANNA- Oh my god. this time what has he seen.

SIDHARTHA- Channa. the man is lying still, but the people around him are crying and now where are they carrying him?

CHANNA- That, Prince the person is dead and he is being taken to be burned.

SIDHARTHA- What do you mean by dead? and if they burn his body will it not burn him? please Channa explain what you mean. so, I can understand.

CHANNA- Prince, I will tell you everything. a baby grows into a child and then a young man, who then goes through the joy and happiness of life, bringing up a family, working for a living, growing older and weaker, finally is dead. every person has to die one day.

These words uttered innocently by the charioteer are shocked the Prince deeply.

SIDHARTHA- Do you mean that one day my wife, my child, my friends and I will all be dead?

CHANNA- Yes prince.

SIDHARTH- Let's go.

CHANNA- No Prince. I will take you to another place, a beautiful garden. a grand feast will be ready.

Sidhartha on his way saw a dignified hermit. the first three sites convincingly proved to him the universal ailments of humanity. the fourth signified the means to overcome the ills of life and to attain calm and peace. these four unexpected signs served to increase the urge in him to renounce the world.

SIDHARTHA- Let's go. I'm not interested in anything now. I wonder how people can be so happy when they know that they will die one day. why people bother to dress up, when one day they are going to be consigned to the flames.

Sidharth was lost in his thoughts of old age, sickness, death. he was deeply thinking about the mystery of death.

PALACE SERVENTS- Prince, happy news. princess has given birth to a son.

SIDHARTHA- You go, I will come.

SIDHARTHA- Yashodhara name him Rahula. Rahula means the bondage which has come to me.

The young prince had lost interest in everything. everyone was sad to see the changes in their beloved Siddhartha.

SIDHARTHA- Father give me permission to leave this palace and go somewhere else. I prefer a change of place.

The worried King readily accepted.

KING SHUDHODHANA – If that will make you happy, I give you permission. Ministers keep a close watch and stay near him and take care of him.

SIDHARTHA- What a lovely place.

Sidhartha saw a man and his ox ploughing the fields. He sat down there. He saw the plough cut across the earth. he saw an earthworm thrown out, the small frog hopped down and ate the worm. a snake which was there in a bush gulped the Frog. an eagle swooped down and grabbed the snake and flew away

.

SIDHARTHA- What suffering the creatures go through. I do not like to see this sad and miserable existence in this world.

He sat under of Rose apple tree and started meditating. as he went deep into the suffering he had seen, his mind was more at peace. first time in his life he could feel a sense of peace and serenity. his mind was now relaxed and at ease.

SIDHARTHA- Your eyes are bright and calm. you look peaceful.

MAN- I am tired of the so-called pleasures that were to be found in the company of others. but now I have left my home and live in the forest caves. I wandered around in search of who way to put an end to my sufferings.

SIDHARTHA- Now I have found the true meaning of my life. from now I would start searching for true happiness and find a cure for the sufferings of the world. let me go back to the palace.

SIDHARTHA- Father... father...

KING SHUDHODHANA – Yes son.

SIDHARTHA- I am here with a request.

KING SHUDHODHANA – Don't make a request that will break my heart.

SIDHARTHA- Father, understand, I want to become a homeless wanderer. so that I can search for a path to put an end to all pain and misery in the world. allow me to explore this path.

KING SHUDHODHANA – What will I do now? my fear has come true. Sidharth My dear please forget the idea of leaving the palace. you are still too young to lead the lonely and arduous life of a holy man. put off your decision until you're old enough. moreover, you are the heir to the throne.

SIDHARTHA– I will rule this kingdom if you give me four promises.

KING SHUDHODHANA – What is it?

SIDHARTHA- One, you should never grow old. Two, you should never fall ill. Three, you should not die and four, you should not be in a state of unhappiness even for a moment.

King called for his Minister.

MINISTER- You seem to be deeply disturbed. can I help you my lord?

KING SHUDHODHANA – Minister we meet to watch Siddhartha. develop the security. I want you to guard the Prince round-the-clock. the prince should not be allowed to leave the palace for any reason. that is my order.
The minister visited Sidharth.

SIDHARTH- Minister, please come in.

MINISTER- Prince your father has passed orders that you should not leave this palace.

SIDHARTH- I am really upset. why does he not understand me?

The same night the sufferings of illness, death, misery and old age kept going around in his mind.

SIDHARTH- I have made up my mind. tonight, somehow, I have to leave this palace. after dinner when I leave this palace, the doors are heavily guarded.

When Sidhartha neared Yashodhar's chamber.

SIDHARTHA- I must see my son. oh, she is sleeping. if I lift the prince's hand to take my son in my arms she will awaken and my departure will be hampered. but I find the truth, I will come back and see him.

By the time Sidharth reach the entrance. all the guards were found sleeping. A super natural power has put all the guards into such a profound sleep that no sound whatsoever would awaken them.

SIDHARTHA- Channa, Channa wake up.

CHANNA- Prince what are you doing here at this midnight hour?

SIDHARTH- Shh… do not make noise. bring my horse. I feel like going for a ride.

CHANNA- Yes, Prince wait here. I'll be back in a moment.

Channa was in a trance and carried out the orders of Sidharth.

Sidharth rode on his horse and Channa followed him. They rode up quietly into the dark. On reaching the edge of the city the prince took a look back.

SIDHARTHA- I will not return to Kapilavastu until I found the means to end all the agony of the world.

They journeyed all night and at dawn neared the dwelling of many holy people. the prince was happy to start with is real journey.

SIDHARTH- Channa thanks for all your help. now take this horse and go back to the palace.

CHANNA- What? am I going back without you? I can't bear this.

SIDHARTH- Please do not cry Channa. I can understand your grief. take all these jewels. I do not need them anymore and tell my father that, I have not left them in anger. I still love them. I'm leaving because I love them most. when I finished my search, I will return to them.

Channa took the reins of Kantaka and slowly let the horse back to the palace. finally, he reached the capital.

KING SHUDHODHANA – Channa, where were you? we were searching for you. hope you know the where abouts of our prince.

CHANNA- He... he has left us. he had renounced royal life forever.

Thank You!

Printed in Great Britain
by Amazon